Chapter 1

I KNOW THE LAST TWENTY-FOUR HOURS HAVE PROBABLY BEEN VERY CONFUSING FOR YOU. YOU MUST HAVE MANY QUESTIONS—

—AND I'M GOING TO ANSWER THEM.

LIKE WHAT WAS THAT CRAP YOU JUST MADE US DRINK?

BUT FIRST, I NEED YOU TO HAND OVER THE GAUNTLET SO THAT WE CAN DESTROY IT.

YEAHHH, WE **COULD** DO THAT.

BUT MAYBE YOU SHOULD TELL US A LITTLE ABOUT THIS ORGANIZATION OF YOURS FIRST.

TAAKO
RACE ELF
CLASS WIZARD
+ PROFICIENCIES +
→ Spell-casting
→ Sizzling things up
→ Snark

THE BUREAU OF BALANCE—OF WHICH I AM THE DIRECTOR—HAS A SINGULAR PURPOSE.

AND THAT IS TO COLLECT... WELL...

...LET'S CALL THEM "WEAPONS OF MASS DESTRUCTION."

I SUPPOSE YOU COULD CALL US A "DISARMAMENT" ORGANIZATION, DEDICATED TO FINDING AND NEUTRALIZING DANGEROUS MAGICAL ARTIFACTS.

ARTIFACTS LIKE THAT GAUNTLET.

the DIRECTOR
RACE HUMAN
+ PROFICIENCIES +
→ Seeing the bigger picture
→ Making the tough call
→ Looking imperious and shit

PHOENIX FIRE GAUNTLET
+ POWER +
→ Off-the-scale fire damage
→ This ain't no oven mitt

PAY THE MEN, DAVENPORT. PAY THEM FOR A GOOD DAY'S WORK.

IT WAS MORE THAN *A* DAY.

MORE LIKE A WEEK, RIGHT?

WE HAD A COUPLE OF PLANNING DAYS, AND WE HAD TO GET THE SUPPLY CHAIN IN ORDER...

TEN? SHOULD WE GO WITH TEN DAYS?

YES! ALL RIGHT! TEN DAYS!

DAVENPORT, PAY THEM FOR THEIR...TEN DAYS OF WORK.

DAVENPORT!

GREAT, THAT'S DONE.

NOW:

WHAT THE *HELL* WAS IN THOSE VIALS?!

YEAH, AND WHAT'S UP WITH YOUR WEIRD-YET-BEAUTIFUL PET IN THE GINORMOUS TANK?

AND I'M NOT SAYING YOU'RE FULL OF IT OR ANYTHING, BUT IF THESE ARTIFACTS WERE HOT SHIT...

...WHY DON'T I REMEMBER HEARING ABOUT THEM?

WHAT WE DO WOULD...NOT BE POSSIBLE WITHOUT THE VOIDFISH.

THE WAR, CALAMITY, AND TURMOIL YOU CAN NOW REMEMBER WAS A DIRECT RESULT OF DANGEROUS MAGICAL ARTIFACTS.

WHEN THESE ITEMS WERE CRAFTED AND WORD OF THEIR POWER SPREAD, EVERYONE WANTED THEM.

EVERY KINGDOM IN THE LAND, EVERY POLITICAL ORGANIZATION, MERCENARY GUILD, RELIGIOUS COMMUNITY...

THEY ALL MOUNTED EFFORTS TO CLAIM THE ARTIFACTS FOR THEIR OWN.

THAT LED TO A WAR THE LIKES OF WHICH THIS WORLD HAD NEVER SEEN.

AND THE ONLY WAY TO END THAT WAR...

...WAS TO MAKE EVERYONE FORGET THE ARTIFACTS EXISTED.

9

YOU SEE, OUR ORGANIZATION IS MADE UP OF THREE DIVISIONS.

THE FIRST GATHERS INFORMATION ON THE ARTIFACTS. THEY ARE KNOWN AS THE SEEKERS.

THE NEXT—

I KNOW! I KNOW! THEY'RE CALLED THE BEATERS!

AND THEN THE KEEPERS!

AND THE ONES WHO GRAB THE SNITCH! THE SNITCH-GRABBERS!

NO...THE RECLAIMERS.

THE SEEKERS ARE NOT PERMITTED TO COLLECT THE ARTIFACTS. THE RECLAIMERS ARE.

THAT'S THE JOB I'M OFFERING YOU.

DO WE GET A LICENSE TO KILL?

I DON'T—

HOW ABOUT A LICENSE TO CHILL?

THAT BRINGS US TO THE THIRD SECTION: THE REGULATORS.

ANYONE WHO USES INFORMATION GATHERED ABOUT THE ARTIFACTS FOR THEIR OWN WHIM, OR WHO WIELDS AN ARTIFACT, EVEN ONCE...

...WILL BE HUNTED DOWN AND PROPERLY DEALT WITH BY THE REGULATORS.

YOU'VE ALREADY MET OUR BEST REGULATOR...

...KILLIAN.

ANGUS McDONALD

CLASS: BOY DETECTIVE | LEVEL: ?

INVENTORY:
INTERCEPTOR BOOK, CALEB CLEVELAND KID
COP VOL 1-3, MAGNIFYING GLASS, FAMILY
SILVERWARE

"HELLO, SIRS!"

I REMEMBER YOU FROM THE FIRST BOOK!

PLEASE, MAGNUS, MERLE, TAAKO—

THE VERY EXISTENCE OF EVERYTHING WE KNOW AND LOVE MAY HANG IN THE BALANCE.

IS THERE DENTAL?

UH... YES?

COOL.

WE'RE IN.

DAVENPORT!!

GENTLEMEN, YOU ARE HEREBY ACCEPTED AS FULLY FLEDGED MEMBERS OF OUR ORDER.

AND WE ARE PROUD TO PRESENT YOU WITH THESE:

BRACERS OF BALANCE.

BRACERS of BALANCE

+ FUNCTION +
→ Travel globe summoning
→ Oddly, helps carpal tunnel

YOU PEOPLE ARE REALLY INTO ALLITERATION.

THESE HAVE BEEN TAILOR-MADE FOR EACH OF YOU, AND ONCE YOU PUT THEM ON, THEY CAN NEVER BE REMOVED.

I'M WORRIED ABOUT "BRACER STINK." WHAT'S THE POLICY ON THAT? IS THERE SOME KIND OF DETERGENT?

UHHH... EACH INITIATE IS ISSUED A SPECIAL BRUSH...

...SO YOU CAN JUST...GET RIGHT IN THERE AND DO SOME... GROUTING.

GROSS, WHO WOULD EVER—

KLICK!

IT MEANS SO MUCH THAT YOU SHOWED UP TO JOIN IN WELCOMING US TO THE CLUB!

MY PRESENCE HERE IS MORE SYMBOLIC, REALLY.

A REGULATOR IS ALWAYS ON HAND WHEN A RECLAIMER JOINS. IT'S OUR WAY OF SAYING:

"I NOW KNOW YOUR FACE. THAT'LL MAKE IT EASIER TO HUNT YOU DOWN."

OH.

KIND OF AN AGGRESSIVE WORKPLACE ENVIRONMENT YOU GOT HERE.

KLIKK!

SO THAT'S IT? JUST ONE CRUMMY BRACER?

WHERE'S THE COOL WEAPONS AND MAGIC DUDS?

YEAH, WE WERE THINKING WE'D GET MORE THAN THAT...

YOU WILL TAKE THESE THREE TOKENS TO OUR ARTIFICER. HE WILL PROVIDE YOU WITH ADDITIONAL ITEMS.

I HOPE I GET A DOG!

THERE ARE NO DOGS—

—ON THE MOON!

IT'S FOR THEIR OWN GOOD. WE WORRY THAT THEY'LL JUST RUN OFF THE EDGE CHASING A STICK OR SOMETHING.

AND LET'S NOT FORGET—

FINALLY! IS IT GOING TO BE A CHECK? CASH? PROMISSORY NOTE?

OH, GOOD. A FANTASY TRAPPER KEEPER.

THAT WILL GUIDE YOU AS YOU GET TO KNOW THE MOON BASE...

...YOUR NEW HOME.

SURE, SURE.

I'M SEEING MAPS. ROOM SERVICE MENU. LAYOUT OF OUR ROOM—

...WAIT!

"ROOM"?! *SINGULAR*?!

I HAVE TO SHARE WITH THESE GUYS??

BUNKIES!!!!

ISN'T THE WHOLE POINT OF THIS ORGANIZATION TO KEEP PEOPLE FROM GETTING THEIR HANDS ON THIS KIND OF THING?

YES, IT'S TRUE THAT IT'S AGAINST THE STRICTURES OF OUR ORDER TO SPECIFICALLY GIVE OUR MEMBERS MAGICAL ARMAMENTS TO USE IN THE FIELD.

SO INSTEAD... WE LEAVE IT TO FATE.

YEAH, IT'S KIND OF AN ETHICAL WORK-AROUND...BUT WHADDAYA GONNA DO?

ANYBODY FEELING LUCKY? WANNA TAKE A SPIN?

ME! ME! I'LL GO FIRST!!

KLONK!

WHIRROKK!

KA-CHUNK!

OH! THAT'S THE TRUE HEART CLASP!

IT LOOKS VERY DASHING.

PULLING. IT. OFF.

TRUE HEART CLASP
+ DESCRIPTION +
→ Magical aid to knowing someone's intentions
→ Stats +2 and advantage on insight checks

ANYBODY WANNA GO NEXT?

I'LL GIVE IT A TRY.

oof!

WHAD!

IT'S CALLED AN UMBRA STAFF, AN ARCANE FOCUS CREATED BY AN ORDER OF ARTIFICERS CALLED THE UMBRA WIZARDS.

THE "UMBRO WIZARDS"? KNOWN FOR THEIR BAGGY SHORTS AND GREAT SOCCER SKILLS?

UMBRA. THEY SPECIALIZED IN CREATING MAGICAL ITEMS THAT LOOKED LIKE NORMAL, EVERYDAY OBJECTS.

IT CONSUMES THE MAGICAL ESSENCE OF DEFEATED MAGIC USERS. SO FOR MOST SPELLCASTERS, THAT MEANS THEIR MAGIC FOCUS.

THESE ARE QUITE RARE. TAKE GOOD CARE OF IT.

UMBRA STAFF
+ ENCHANTMENT +
→ Sorcerous absorption
→ Rubbing other magic-
   users' noses in it

...AND IT WOULD PROBABLY BE A GOOD IDEA TO NOT LET GARFIELD CATCH A GLIMPSE OF IT.

...WHO?

YOU'LL SEE.

WHAT AN *INTRIGUING* BUMBERSHOOT YOU HAVE THERE!

DON'T YOU WORRY YOUR FURRY LITTLE SELF ABOUT THAT.

YOU'RE PROVIDING US WITH SHIT. NOT THE OTHER WAY AROUND.

FOR NOW...

SO, YOU MUST BE RECENT HIRES? FIRST DAY ON THE MOON?

ALWAYS GREAT TO SEE NEW BLOOD!

"NEW BLOOD"!!!

HAHA HAHAHA!

SEE, IT'S VERY FUNNY IF YOU KNOW I ACCEPT BLOOD AS CURRENCY.

I JUST KILL ME.

AHEM

ALLOW ME TO SUGGEST...

A FEW DAYS AGO, OUR SEEKERS LOCATED ANOTHER ARTIFACT.

THIS WEAPON IS... EVEN MORE POWERFUL, MORE DANGEROUS THAN THE PHOENIX FIRE GAUNTLET.

WE DISPATCHED ONE OF OUR RECLAIMERS TO RETRIEVE IT—A MAN NAMED LEEMAN KESSLER.

AFTER HIS INITIAL REPORT, LEEMAN VIOLATED PROTOCOL BY NOT CHECKING IN AT THE REQUIRED TIME.

WE FEAR HE WAS UNABLE TO RESIST THE THRALL OF THE ARTIFACT.

YEAH, WELL, NOT EVERYBODY'S TAAKO!

YOU ARE CERTAINLY CORRECT THERE.

WHILE I WAS GETTING YOU LOT SET UP WITH HR, THE BUREAU SENT ONE OF MY FELLOW REGULATORS—CAREY FANGBATTLE—TO RECOVER KESSLER FROM HIS LAST KNOWN LOCATION:

THE CITY OF ROCKPORT.

DID SHE FIND HIM?

YEAH, SHE FOUND HIM.

HE WASN'T *BREATHING*, BUT SHE FOUND HIM.

LET ME GUESS...NO WEAPON.

NO WEAPON.

DID THEY FIND ANYTHING?

A LOT OF BLOOD.

OF COURSE. NOBODY EVER DIES OF OLD AGE AROUND YOU PEOPLE.

ALSO A BAGGAGE CAR CLAIM CHECK...

...AND A TRAIN TICKET FOR THE ROCKPORT LIMITED.

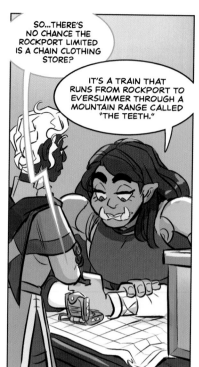

SO...THERE'S NO CHANCE THE ROCKPORT LIMITED IS A CHAIN CLOTHING STORE?

IT'S A TRAIN THAT RUNS FROM ROCKPORT TO EVERSUMMER THROUGH A MOUNTAIN RANGE CALLED "THE TEETH."

WE BELIEVE LEEMAN MANAGED TO SECURE PASSAGE.

THE LUGGAGE CLAIM WOULD INDICATE HE WAS ABLE TO STASH THE ARTIFACT ON THE TRAIN...

BUT HE GOT WHACKED BEFORE THE DEPARTURE.

PUMP THE BRAKES FOR A SECOND THERE, DIRECTOR.

YOU SAID YOU USED SOME HOODOO TO MAKE EVERYONE FORGET THE ARTIFACTS.

IF SO, THEN HOW DID SOMEONE KNOW TO KILL THE VIC AND STEAL THE WEAPON?

WE DON'T KNOW...

WE'RE HOPING IT'S A HORRIBLE COINCIDENCE...

...BECAUSE ANY OTHER ALTERNATIVE IS TOO TERRIFYING TO CONTEMPLATE.

NEVER MIND THAT...

THE TRAIN LEAVES IN TWO HOURS.

ONE OF YOU MUST POSE AS LEEMAN KESS—

GRAB!

"ALAS! POOR YOGI! I KNEW HIM, HORSERADISH!"

"A FELLOW WITH INK ON HIS CHEST—"

FANTASY COSTCO

WE'RE IN KIND OF A RUSH HERE! WE DON'T REALLY HAVE TIME FOR AUDITIONS!

FINE! YOU CAN BE LEEMAN KESSLER!

ACTING! THANK YOU!

hee hee!

YOU NEED TO LOOK LIKE YOU BELONG ON A FANCY TRAIN. GO CHANGE AND THEN GET YOUR ASSES DOWN TO THE HANGAR!

HMMMM... "WARDROBE FITTING."

NOW WE'RE TALKING!

ALL RIGHT, WELL, THE REST OF THIS ORIENTATION AGENDA'S PRETTY MUCH TRASHED.

SO MUCH FOR "MERLE GETS TATTOO REMOVED"!

WHO SCHEDULED THAT?

AND WHY DO THEY HATE KENNY CHESNEY?

"PICK OUT KESSLER PARTY DISGUISES."

CHECK!

"REPORT TO NEW ROOM IN ENTRY-LEVEL DORMS."

CHECK!

"BE UNDERWHELMED"...

CHECK.

THIS CAN'T BE RIGHT.

YOU MUST HAVE BROUGHT US TO THE WRONG PLACE... LIKE...A MOON BASE JAIL CELL.

WHAT? ARE YOU CRAZY? THIS IS *PERFECT!*

THIS IS HOW THEY TREAT HEROES?!

WE BRING THEM A DEADLY FIRE GAUNTLET AND THEY STICK US IN THIS DUMP?

THERE'S NO WAY THEY CAN EXPECT THREE PEOPLE TO LIVE IN THIS ROOM!

THEY DON'T...

...THEY EXPECT *FOUR* PEOPLE TO LIVE IN THIS ROOM.

DON'T TOUCH MY SHIT!! —ROBBIE

UN-BE-LEEV-ABLE!

OH, I DON'T KNOW...

...I KIND OF LIKE HIS STYLE.

HEY, FELLAS!!

THESE DISGUISES ARE *AWESOME!*

OH, YEAH.

I'M GONNA NEED TO LIVE OFF-CAMPUS.

AVI IS WAITING FOR YOU IN THE CANNON BAY.

IF YOU LEAVE NOW YOU SHOULD HAVE JUST ENOUGH TIME TO CLAIM KESSLER'S LUGGAGE BEFORE THE TRAIN LEAVES THE STATION.

YOU CAN USE YOUR BRACERS TO CALL FOR A TRANSPORT SPHERE ONCE YOU HAVE THE ARTIFACT IN HAND.

HOLD UP...

..."CANNON BAY"?

AH.

YES, I SHOULD WARN YOU, THE BUREAU'S MAIN MEANS OF CONVEYANCE IS...

...PRETTY INTENSE.

SHIT...SERIOUSLY? THOSE ARE *TRANSPORTATION* CANNONS?

HUH. I THOUGHT THEY WERE FOR MOON-BASE-TO-MOON-BASE COMBAT OR SOMETHING.

ONE MORE THING...

THE MAGIC USERS WHO CREATED THIS WEAPON...THEY'RE CALLED...RED ROBES, NAMED AFTER THE BRIGHT CRIMSON GARMENTS THEY WEAR.

AS YOU MIGHT GUESS, THEY'RE INCREDIBLY DANGEROUS INDIVIDUALS.

IF YOU COME ACROSS ANY OF THEM IN THIS MISSION, IT'S *IMPERATIVE* THAT YOU—

...

WHAT'S *THIS* ONE DO?!

DOES THIS BAD BOY HAVE NITROUS?!

TOO FAST!! TOO FURIOUS!!

THIS WILL BE A LOT MORE... UNCOMFORTABLE THAN YOUR LAST RIDE. A LOT OF FORCE.

YEAH, YEAH, YEAH! LET'S JUST GET THIS OVER WITH!

I DON'T SEE ANY CUP HOLDERS.

AVI
DESIGNATION
LAUNCH SPECIALIST
+ PROFICIENCIES +
→ PERIGREES
→ APOGEES
→ HERO WORSHIP

BUT LISTEN, IT IS *VITALLY IMPORTANT* THAT ONE OF YOU SIT IN THAT SEAT.

THIS IS A FANTASY AIR BRAKE.

IF YOU PULL IT TOO EARLY, THE MOMENTUM DISRUPTION MAGIC WILL FADE.

AND THAT WOULD BE BAD.

SURE, SURE. GOT IT.

Chapter 2

YOU'VE GOT A HELL OF A LOT OF ARMED BEEF STATIONED HERE, THOMAS. SOMETHING WE NEED TO KNOW?

OH, NO, SIR, NOTHING TO CONCERN YOURSELVES ABOUT!

NOTHING WRONG HERE! JUST ANOTHER TYPICAL, MURDER-FREE DAY IN ROCKPORT!!

TO LIMIT ACCESS, OUR STATE-OF-THE-ART CARGO CAR IS AT THE VERY REAR OF THE TRAIN.

NO WINDOWS, WHICH KEEPS IT EVEN MORE SECURE FROM MARAUDERS...

...NOT THAT THEY'LL BE ANY PROBLEM...

...THANKS TO THE CRYPTSAFE.

CRYPTSAFE
TOP-OF-THE-LINE SECURITY DEVICE

THE CRYPTSAFE IS INDESTRUCTIBLE AND BUILT INTO THE VERY FLOOR OF THE CAR.

IMPRESSIVE!

LET ME VIEW MY PROPERTY, SIR.

AFRAID THAT'S NOT POSSIBLE, MR. KESSLER. YOUR ITEMS HAVE ALREADY BEEN STOWED IN THE CRYPTSAFE.

IT'S TIME-LOCKED. IT WILL ONLY OPEN AFTER AN EMPLOYEE OF THE RAILROAD— SPECIFICALLY, THE ENGINEER, MR. HUDSON—MAINTAINS SUSTAINED PHYSICAL CONTACT WITH IT...

...FOR AN HOUR.

IT WAS A GOOD THOUGHT.

46

IS THAT SHAG CARPET?

THIS IS A FULL-OPTION TRAIN, MY DUDES, FULLY LUXURIED OUT.

THIS IS THE LEXUS OF FANTASY TRAINS. GILDED FEATURES. POSH INTERIOR.

YES, IT IS. GOOD EYE, SIR.

I AM HUDSON, YOUR ENGINEER. WELCOME ABOARD. WE'RE HAPPY TO HAVE YOU.

HUDSON,
Race   ELF
Class   ENGINEER
(NOT THE BRIDGE-BUILDING, TUNNEL-DIGGING KIND...THE "MAKING THE TRAIN GO" KIND)
+ PROFICIENCIES +
→ Toeing the corporate line
→ Railway navigation
→ Doing the loco-motion

WE KNOW YOU HAVE A LOT OF CHOICES FOR SUBTERRANEAN INTER-CITY TRAVEL, AND WE APPRECIATE THAT YOU CHOSE US!

WELL, THANK YOU FOR HAVING US ON YOUR EXQUISITE CHOO-CHOO.

YOU'RE IN LUCK. WE'RE RIDING LIGHT, SO YOU'LL HAVE YOUR PICK OF SEATING IN THE PASSENGER CAR.

AND HERE WE ARE AT THE ENGINE CAR. THIS IS WHERE I WILL BE FOR THE DURATION OF THE TRIP.

AS A SECURITY MEASURE, I WILL NOT BE COMING OUT AGAIN UNTIL WE ARRIVE AT EVERSUMMER.

THIS IS ALSO WHERE I MUST ASK YOU FOR—

OUR TICKETS? OF COURSE!

NO, SIR.

YOUR WEAPONS, PLEASE.

UHHH...NO.

NO, THANK YOU. I DON'T BELIEVE I WANT TO DO THAT.

MOUNTAIN TRAIN SECURITY AGENCY PROTOCOLS DEMAND THAT ALL WEAPONS BE LOCKED UP WITH ME IN THE ENGINE CAR.

GOODBYE, SMOOSHER.

GOODBYE, LIL CHOPPY.

IS IT OKAY IF I KEEP MY UMBRELLA IN CASE OF A STORM?

WELL, WE'LL BE INSIDE A TRAIN INSIDE A GIANT MOUNTAIN RANGE, SO NOT MUCH CHANCE OF RAIN, BUT...SURE!

VISIT SCENIC GOLDCLIFF

PAID FOR BY THE GOLDCLIFF TRUST

ALL RIGHT, BUT I HAVE TO HANG ON TO MY GAUNTLET. I HAVE...STINKY HAND SYNDROME.

HE'S NOT KIDDING. THE STENCH WILL HAUNT YOUR DREAMS.

FINE.

BUT YOU HAVE TO DO ONE THING FOR ME!

WHAT'S THAT?

LET ME SIT ON YOUR LAP AND STEER?

WHOOMSHLAM!!

HUDSON THE ENGINEER, LADIES AND GENTLEMEN!!

WE HOPE YOU ENJOYED HIM! WE'LL SEE HIM AGAIN AT THE END OF THE LINE!

HE WASN'T KIDDING ABOUT IT NOT BEING VERY FULL.

AND TWO OF THEM ARE DWARVES!

LOOK CLOSER...

...I THINK THE LITTLEST ONE IS A KID.

YOU DON'T THINK THAT'S WEIRD? SOME LITTLE KID TRAVELING BY HIMSELF ON A TRAIN?

HE'S PERFECTLY FINE, SIR...

...THE ROCKPORT LIMITED IS PERFECTLY SAFE.

MY NAME IS JENKINS. YOUR WIZARD ATTENDANT FOR THIS TRIP.

JENKINS
RACE ELF
CLASS
EITHER A WIZARD WHO'S AN ATTENDANT OR AN ATTENDANT TO WIZARDS
+ PROFICIENCIES +
+ GASTRONOMY
+ PERSONAL SERVICE
+ HORTICULTURE

I LIKE YOUR TIE, JENKINS. TELL ME ABOUT IT.

YOU HAVE AN EYE FOR THE FINER THINGS, SIR.

THIS IS MY... FLAIR. WE ALL GET TO WEAR ONE PIECE OF FLAIR ON TUESDAYS.

GOOD GOD! MORE BUNK BEDS!

IT'S AS IF EVERY DECORATOR IN THIS REALITY SPENT WAY TOO MUCH TIME AT SUMMER CAMP!

SO ARE YOU AN ATTENDANT WHO'S A WIZARD, OR AN ATTENDANT **TO** A WIZARD—

I AM A WIZARD WHO MUST ATTEND TO THE NEEDS OF THE PASSENGERS ON THE TRAIN.

AND I HAVE A FEW LUXURY SERVICES I CAN PROVIDE.

FOR INSTANCE, I CAN TAKE YOU INTO OUR PLEASURE CHAMBER.

SORRY TO DISAPPOINT, BUT IT'S NOT A SEX THING.

MY SOFT, SENSUOUS VOICE JUST MAKES EVERYTHING SOUND SALACIOUS. IT'S A CURSE.

THE PLEASURE CHAMBER IS A RECREATIONAL TELEPORTATION EXPERIENCE THAT ALLOWS PASSENGERS TO BRIEFLY VISIT ANY ENCLOSED SPACE OF THEIR CHOOSING ANYWHERE IN THE WORLD.

THE SPELL IS POWERFUL BUT LIMITED. YOU CAN'T BRING ANYTHING BACK THROUGH THE PORTAL...OR LEAVE ANYTHING THERE.

JUST IN CASE YOU WERE THINKING OF DOING ANY, YOU KNOW, SMUGGLING.

LEEMAN KESSLER IS NO SMUGGLER!!

LIKE YOU'D KNOW.

51

YES, I'M SURE YOU WOULD. BUT THERE'S NO CHANCE OF THAT DURING THIS TRIP.

IT'S LOCKED UP WITH HUDSON. I HAD TO LUG THE DAMNED THING UP THERE MYSELF.

KIND OF A SHITTY WIZARD.

I'M SORRY...SIR?

JUST CAST A SPELL OF LEVITATION! THAT'S SECOND LEVEL STUFF, MY MAN!

OH, I'M SORRY.

I DIDN'T REALIZE THAT LIFE ON THE RAILS WAS SO *DEMANDING* YOU NEED PYROTECHNICS AT YOUR FINGERTIPS TWENTY-FOUR-SEV!

WHAT AM I GOING TO DO? BURN ONE OF MY DAILY SLOTS ON LEVITATING AN AX?

YOU SHOULD DO WHAT I DO: HAVE UNLIMITED SPELL SLOTS AND USE EVERY SPELL IN THE BOOK!

THAT'S CALLED "CHEATING," ACTUALLY.

YEAH...WELL...

WE WOULDN'T WANT TO DO THAT... WOULD WE?

MAYBE YOU JUST NEED TO LIVE LIFE A LITTLE! GET OUT IN THE WORLD AND LEVEL UP! THAT'S ALL I'M SAYING.

I HAVE NO INTEREST IN YOUR LIFE HACKS.

BACK THERE IS THE KITCHEN.

I AM ALSO THE CHEF ON THIS TRIP. NOW THAT I KNOW YOU, I'LL BE SURE TO BAKE A LOT OF LOVE INTO WHATEVER YOU ORDER.

YOU SAVING YOUR SPELLS FOR THAT?

OF COURSE, BEYOND THE KITCHEN IS THE CARGO CAR. I'M SURE YOU'VE BEEN BRIEFED ON ALL THE SECURITY PROTOCOLS.

NO DOUBT MOST OF IT SAILED OVER YOUR HEADS—

JENKINS, COULD YOU PLEASE OPEN THE WINDOW?

CERTAINLY, SIR.

BUT BY ALL MEANS, DON'T BURN A SPELL SLOT ON IT.

HA!

NOW SEE HERE!

I LIVE TO SERVE THE PEOPLE ON THIS TRAIN! AND YOU CRETINS—!!

EASY, JENKINS! WE'RE JUST JOSHIN'!

PLEASE, GENTLEMEN, WE REALLY MUST MOVE AHEAD WITH THE TOUR.

IT'S NEARLY NOON...

...AND THAT'S "JENKINS' TIME."

AS IN—?

AS IN "JENKINS' TIME...

"...TO START FIXING...

"...YOUR BRUNCH."

SLAM!!

Chapter 3

EXCUSE ME, FANCY LAD...

HOW WOULD YOU LIKE TO BE A "PAN-CY" LAD?

I'D LIKE TO TELL YOU ABOUT MY GOOD FRIEND PAN.

ESPECIALLY ONES WHO WORSHIP OLYMPIAN GODS.

THANK YOU FOR THE EVANGELISM, SIR, BUT MY GRANDPA ALWAYS TOLD ME I SHOULDN'T TALK TO STRANGERS...

WELL, I NOTICED YOU'RE READING. PERHAPS YOU'D LIKE TO READ THIS CHICK TRACT.

YOU CAN CALL ME BROTHER LEEMAN.

THIS KID IS DEFINITELY THE BAD GUY.

MY NAME'S ANGUS. ANGUS MCDONALD.

I'M GOING TO VISIT MY GRANDPA IN EVERSUMMER.

ANGUS MCDONALD
RACE HUMAN
CLASS unaccompanied minor
+ PROFICIENCIES +
→ Being adorable
→ Reading, at a high school level
→ snack consumption

I CAN'T WAIT TO READ YOUR VERY SMALL PAMPHLET DRAWN IN A SIMPLE STYLE REMINISCENT OF UNDERGROUND COMICS! I LOVE TO READ!

SEE? WHAT LITTLE KID LIKES TO READ?!

HE IS SO-O-O-O THE BAD GUY.

IF YOU SIRS WILL EXCUSE ME...

I CAME HERE TO READ BOOKS AND CHEW BUBBLE GUM, AND I'M ALL OUT OF GUM.

THANK YOU FOR THE GOOD CHAT.

WOW...

...THIS THING'S AMAZING!

THIS *TRAIN* IS AMAZING!!

DON'T YOU GUYS LOVE BEING ON THIS TRAIN? THIS TRAIN'S THE BEST!

EH, I'VE SEEN BETTER.

MY NAME'S GRAHAM. AND YOU ARE...?

GRAHAM
RACE HUMAN
CLASS WIZARD
+ PROFICIENCIES +
→ Train obsession
→ Dodgy fashion choices
→ Panic

I WOULD LOVE TO WORK ON A TRAIN. IT'S BEEN MY DREAM TO LIVE A LIFE ON THE RAILS!

AS A MATTER OF FACT, I APPLIED FOR A JOB WITH THE ROCKPORT LIMITED BUT DIDN'T GET ACCEPTED.

MOTIVE! HE HAD MOTIVE!

MOTIVE FOR *WHAT?*

MURDER! *MURDER MOST FOUL.*

OH, SLOW YOUR ROLL, COLUMBO.

I JUST CAME ON THIS TRIP TO SHADOW JENKINS AND SEE WHAT I COULD LEARN. PICK UP A FEW POINTERS.

YOU MEAN.. YOU'RE A WORSE WIZARD...THAN *JENKINS?*

I'M STANDING *RIGHT HERE!*

YOU PURPOSELY SAID THAT LOUD ENOUGH FOR ME TO HEAR! WHY WOULD YOU DO THAT?!

I WAS BEING THOUGHTFUL!

I DIDN'T WANT YOU TO WASTE A *PRECIOUS SPELL SLOT* TRYING TO READ MY MIND!

AWK-WARD...

CRUNCH CRUMPLE

SLURP

WE ARE REEEEALLY MAKING FRIENDS ON THIS TRAIN.

I HAD A TRICKED-OUT WAGON, PULLED BY A COUPLE OF BEAUTIFUL HORSES: ALTON AND NIGELLA.

I JUST HAD TO HIT A COUPLE OF SWITCHES AND VOILÀ! MY WHOLE SETUP, RIGHT THERE ON THE ROAD!

AHHHH, IT WAS A THING OF BEAUTY, MERLE!

THE WHOLE RIG WAS PRETTY PRICEY, BUT IT WAS WORTH EVERY CENT.

OH! IT WAS A MONEY-MAKING THING!

I THOUGHT IT WAS SOME KIND OF ART FORM!

IT WAS, THE WAY *I* DID IT!

UH, HELLO?

ISN'T IT TIME WE GOT BACK TO SOLVING *THE CASE*?!

GIVE IT A REST!!

PLEASURE CHAMBER
+ POWER +
+ TRANSPORT
TO OTHER LOCATIONS
+ IT TOTALLY CAN BE A
SEX THING

FOR SUCH A SOPHISTICATED TELEPORTATION MAGIC, YOU'D HAVE TO USE SOMETHING TO FOCUS IT...

TAP TAP

TELEPORT ROD?

YES INDEED. IT WORKS IN CONCERT WITH THE CHAMBER.

TELEPORT ROD
+POWER+
activates teleportation magic

THAT'S AN ASTUTE OBSERVATION FOR HIRED MUSCLE.

JENKINS, OLD PAL—

CALEB CLEVELAN AND THE TOMB OF HORR

TOMB

CALEB

DON'T JUDGE A BOOK BY ITS BREATHTAKINGLY ATTRACTIVE COVER.

WHAT WILL IT BE, GENTLEMEN?

A DAY SPA AT SWORD BEACH? THE MINSKER POOL HALL IN GOLDCLIFF?

I KNOW!

I WANT YOU TO SEND ME...

TO OUR SLEEPER CAR!

HERF

SNRK

YOU WANT ME TO USE... MY INCREDIBLE TELEPORTATION MAGIC...

TO GO INTO THE ROOM THAT IS ADJACENT TO THE ROOM WE'RE CURRENTLY IN?

WHAT ABOUT YOUR MOM'S HOUSE—?

HOW DO YOU KNOW MY—

—AGAIN?

OH... I SEE.

IS THIS A REAL REQUEST OR ONE OF YOUR...HILARIOUS "BURNS," SIR?

SEE? NOW YOU'RE GETTING IT!

GOOD-NATURED RIBBING! THAT'S HOW YOU KNOW YOU'RE ONE OF THE GANG!

JUST SEND US TO YOUR FAVORITE PLACE.

KLAP

HEE HEE

VWOOORP!

HELLO, SIRS.

HOW WAS YOUR TRIP?

VERY PLEASURABLE! BUT WE SURE MISSED *YOU.*

YOU DID? THAT'S NICE, SIRS!

AND SINCE WE'RE ALL GETTING SO CLOSE...

...MAYBE YOU WOULD BE WILLING TO TELL ME YOUR *REAL* NAMES?

SAY WHA–?

'SCUSE?

WHAT DO YOU MEAN, PUMPKIN?

YOUR *REAL* NAMES. WHAT YOU CALL YOURSELF WHEN YOU'RE *NOT* PRETENDING TO BE LEEMAN KESSLER.

WHO WAS MURDERED RECENTLY, DID YOU KNOW THAT?

WE KNOW THAT. HOW DO *YOU* KNOW THAT?

BECAUSE I'M...

–the WORLD'S GREATEST DETECTIVE!!!

ANGUS McDONALD
Race Human
Class WORLD'S GREATEST detective (self-proclaimed)
→ PROFICIENCIES ←
→ Keen Observation
→ Analytical mind
→ Keeping secrets

HANG ON, IS THIS SUPPOSED TO BE USEFUL? I CAN'T MAKE IT OUT AT **ALL!**

WELL, OF COURSE— THE BOOK PICKS UP AN UNFILTERED MAGICAL STREAM!

I SIMPLY FILTERED OUT ANYTHING WITH AN ORIGIN BEYOND ROCKPORT'S GEOMAGICAL COORDINATES, CLUSTERED RECORDS SENT WITHIN THE PERIOD JUST BEFORE EMBARKATION, TWEAKED A BASIC NLP TOOLKIT TO FLAG ANY UNEXPECTED REFERENCES TO PASSENGERS, AND APPLIED THAT TO THE INCOMING DATA...

...TO PARSE THE RELEVANT MESSAGE.

CRITERIA:
☑ HAS- PASS-NAMES
☑ ROCKPORT GMC
MESSAGES FOUND: 1

THOMAS|13:05:02
LEEMAN KESSLER AND CO. NOT WHO THEY SAY THEY ARE -STOP- CHARM MAGIC SPELL PERFORMED ON ME AT THE STATION -STOP- HAND OVER TO AUTHORITIES IMMEDIATELY UPON ARRIVAL IN EVERSUMMER -STOP-

WELL, IF IT WERE EASY, YOU WOULDN'T HAVE TO BE THE WORLD'S GREATEST DETECTIVE TO USE IT!!

I **KNEW** WE SHOULD HAVE MADE THAT THOMAS GUY WALK IN FRONT OF A TRAIN!

THIS KID SEEMS TO HAVE HIS SHIT TOGETHER. HE COULD BE A REAL ASSET TO ME AS I SOLVE THIS MYSTERY.

YOU SOLVE—

ALL RIGHT, KID...

...LET'S GO HAVE A PRIVATE CONVO.

Chapter 4

THE ROCKPORT CITY COUNCIL WANTS ME TO TRACK DOWN THE PERSON WHO HAS BEEN KILLING LOCAL WEALTHY INDIVIDUALS FOR THE PAST FEW MONTHS.

THE SLAYER MURDERS THEM AND STEALS THEIR RICHES...AND NEVER LEAVES A TRACE.

GOOD LUCK! –R.C.C.

BUT *I* AM GOING TO *STOP* THIS LUNATIC!

YES...*WE* WILL STOP THAT LUNATIC.

WE'LL HAVE TO LOOK AT OUR SUSPECT LIST.

I GUESS A TRIO OF DESPERATE HARD-ASSES LIKE US ARE RIGHT AT THE TOP OF THAT LIST, HUH, KID?

OH, NO, SIR.

I AM A HUNDRED PERCENT SURE THAT THE THREE OF YOU DON'T POSSESS THE COMPETENCY REQUIRED TO PERFORM MULTIPLE MURDERS WITHOUT GETTING CAUGHT.

PRETTY SOLID OBSERVATION.

HE *IS* A GOOD DETECTIVE!

HOWEVER, THE FACT THAT YOU SHOWED UP POSING AS LEEMAN KESSLER INDICATES YOU ARE ALSO LOOKING FOR HIS KILLER...

...OR HIS *TREASURE!*

YOU TOLD HIM THERE'S A TREASURE?!

I DIDN'T SAY NUTHIN' ABOUT NO TREASURE!

WHY DO YOU THINK THERE'S A TREASURE?

THAT'S THE ROCKPORT SLAYER'S M.O.

HE KILLS, THEN STEALS HIS VICTIM'S MOST VALUABLE POSSESSION...

...AND *THAT'S* WHY YOU'RE ON THE TRAIN.

I THINK WE'RE WORKING TOWARD A SIMILAR GOAL.

THE THREE OF US WORK FOR AN ORGANIZATION—

WHAT ORGANIZATION? FANTASY C.S.I.? FANTASY S.H.I.E.L.D.? FANTASY MALL COPS?

THE *BUREAU OF BALANCE.*

...I... COULDN'T QUITE CATCH THAT, SIR...?

NOT THIS SHIT AGAIN...

81

I WOULD BE WILLING TO BET THAT WE ALSO CAN'T TELL YOU THAT WE'RE TRYING TO RECOVER "A DANGEROUS MAGICAL ARTIFACT"!

"DANGEROUS MAGICAL ARTIFACT," GOT YOU LOUD AND CLEAR!

HM...SO THERE'S THIS MOON BASE AND DOGS AREN'T ALLOWED THERE...?

FWUMP.

DO THOSE COMMUNICATION BRACERS PREVENT ME FROM UNDERSTANDING WHAT YOU ARE TRYING TO SAY?

SURE, LET'S GO WITH THAT.

ANGUS, HERE'S WHAT WE CAN TELL YOU:

THIS ITEM, IF IT FALLS INTO THE WRONG HANDS, IS REMARKABLY DANGEROUS. IT'S INCREDIBLY BAD.

THE BODY COUNT FOR THIS SLAYER PERSON WOULD INCREASE FROM DOZENS TO THOUSANDS IN SHORT ORDER.

WE NEED TO WORK TOGETHER AND FIGURE THIS OUT NOW!

I AGREE. THAT'S WHY I'M ENLISTING YOU TO HELP ME APPREHEND THE ROCKPORT SLAYER...

WHO MUST BE SOMEWHERE ON THIS TRAIN!

IF MY SUSPICIONS ARE TO BE BELIEVED, THE ITEM YOU SEEK IS INSIDE THE CARGO CAR CRYPTSAFE.

BRUSH BRUSH

NOW YOU'RE JUST SHOWBOATING, KID. THAT'S WHERE THEY LOCK STUFF UP ON THIS TRAIN.

YOU DIDN'T REALLY, LIKE, DEDUCE THE SHIT OUT OF THAT ONE.

DULY NOTED, SIRS.

BUT I SUSPECT IT WILL REQUIRE EVERY ONE OF MY LITTLE GRAY CELLS...

...TO IDENTIFY THE ROCKPORT SLAYER.

83

ffwwwsssh!

Chapter 5

MS. BEHEADER, MAY I JUST SAY: I LOVE YOUR WORK!

I HAD BOTH OF YOUR ACTION FIGURES: THE CHAMPIONSHIP BELT VERSION AND THE HARD-TO-FIND BLOOD-SPLATTERED VERSION!

ALWAYS NICE TO MEET A FAN.

I HAVE TO SAY, THAT "GLOWING SPIRITUAL AX" THING WAS PRETTY DAMN SWEET!

KID HAS A CROSSBOW. SHE'S GOT AN AX...PRETTY FLEXIBLE NO-WEAPONS POLICY THIS TRAIN HAS!

OH, IT'S NOT SPIRITUAL, IT'S JUST SOULBOUND TO ME. I CAN SUMMON IT WHENEVER I NEED IT.

CAN I TRY IT?

...IT'S NOT SOULBOUND TO YOU.

WE CAN DO THE BLOOD BROTHER THING! CUT OUR PALMS, SHAKE HANDS...THEN I'LL BE SOULBOUNDED, TOO, RIGHT?

...NO.

BESIDES, THE AX IS KINDA MY "JAM."

EVERYBODY IN THE MIDWORLD WRESTLING FEDERATION HAS A GIMMICK.

MINE HAPPENS TO BE A MAGNIFICENT SOULBOUND AX THAT SPRINGS TO MY SIDE WHEN THERE'S GREAT DANGER.

YEAAAHHH.

CAN'T HELP BUT NOTICE...

...IT'S STILL HERE.

109

WE FOUND YOU IN THE CONNECTING CAR WITH JENKINS' CORPSE. DID YOU SEE WHAT HAPPENED?

I WENT TO FIND JENKINS TO ASK HIM IF I COULD TAKE ANOTHER ROUND IN THE PLEASURE CHAMBER.

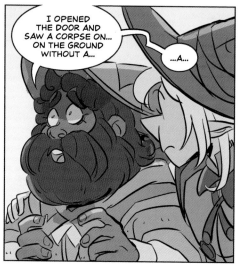

I OPENED THE DOOR AND SAW A CORPSE ON... ON THE GROUND WITHOUT A...

...A...

ahhhhh

YOU DON'T GET OUT OF THIS BY FAINTING, JUICY!

BWAP

3.5%.

WHEN YOU SAW THE BODY...DID IT HAVE HANDS?

NO! IT WAS AWFUL!

AND I'D SEEN JENKINS ONLY A FEW MINUTES EARLIER, PROVIDING DRINK SERVICE...

LISTEN TO ME CAREFULLY, BECAUSE THIS NEXT PART IS EXTREMELY IMPORTANT.

DID YOU NOTICE JENKINS SETTING ASIDE ANY DRINKS FOR SOMEONE?

OR DID ANYONE TAKE AN EXTRA DRINK FOR LATER?

IS THERE SOMEWHERE ON THIS TRAIN I CAN FIND SOME DRINKS!!!

THE DRINK CART?!!!

THE DRINK CART IS GONE!

GONE!!

IT'S HITTING US ALL PRETTY HARD, BUD.

WE'LL HAVE TO HELP EACH OTHER THROUGH THIS.

HE'S TELLING THE TRUTH.

I WAS HERE THE WHOLE TIME.

GRAHAM WALKED BACK THERE AND WENT THROUGH THE DOOR.

WHEN THE DOOR SHUT I HEARD A SHRIEK...LIKE SOME SMALL CHILD. THOUGHT HE WAS JUST HAVING A CONNIPTION.

YOU, UHH.

DIDN'T HAPPEN TO... MURDER JENKINS, DID YOU, JESS?

EX*CUSE* ME?

I ONLY ASK BECAUSE OF THE WHOLE "BEHEADER" THING...

...YOU KNOW: JESS THE *BEHEADER....?* JUST TRYING TO BE THOROUGH.

IT'S A STAGE NAME! FOR THE JOB! WHAT DO *YOU* DO FOR A LIVING?

DO YOU "WIZARD" IN YOUR FREE TIME? I ONLY BEHEAD PEOPLE WHEN I *NEED* TO!

I'M A CHEF...UH, WIZARD. SORT OF A CHEF-WIZARD HYBRID.

OR WHEN I'M GETTING PAID FOR IT...

...YOU KNOW...FOR ENTERTAINMENT.

THIS IS GOOD! THIS IS GOOD!

SHOVE!

THE THREE OF US WERE WITH ANGUS. JESS AND GRAHAM WERE TOGETHER IN THE PASSENGER CAR...

AND JENKINS WAS SERVING THEM DRINKS—

YEAH, RIGHT AFTER HE TOOK THE DRINK CART UP TO THE ENGINEER CAR.

117

GREAT!

TELL US!

ISN'T IT MORE FUN IF YOU FIGURE IT OUT FOR YOURSELVES?

NO, AS A MATTER OF FACT, IT ISN'T!

SO, IS IT—

I DON'T ACTUALLY KNOW!! I WAS TRYING TO IMPRESS YOU!!

I THOUGHT YOU WERE THE WORLD'S GREATEST DETECTIVE!

YEAH, BUT I'M NOT *PSYCHIC!*

EXCUSES, EXCUSES.

ALL-RIGHTY, THEN. YOUR TURN, JESS. SHOW US WHAT'S IN YOUR POCKETS.

UHHHHH...

NO.

DAMN! I REALLY THOUGHT THAT WAS GOING TO WORK. NOW WHAT?

WAIT!

I ACTUALLY HAVE A SPELL THAT WILL HELP!

I CAST DISCERNMENT OF MAGICKS!

DISCERNMENT *of* MAGICKS

hoity-toity way of saying "Locate things with magic all over them"

HEY, ARE THOSE MAGICAL LOAFERS?

YEAH...BUT DON'T BRING IT UP.

WELL, NO SIGN OF THE ROD...THAT MEANS NO KILLER.

ONLY ONE PLACE LEFT TO CHECK—

THE CARGO CAR!

SKUKLY SKUDDY SKUDDLE!

skuddle-BUZZZ!

skuddle SNUGGLE!

WHY DOES IT HAVE TO FEEL SO STICKY?

HOW'S THE ODD COUPLE BACK THERE?

GRAHAM HASN'T SHUT UP SINCE WE LEFT.

RIGHT NOW HE'S ASKING JESS TO BE CAREFUL WITH THE AX BECAUSE HE'S A BLEEDER.

HEE HEE!

TO OPEN THE CRYPTSAFE, A ROCKPORT EMPLOYEE HAS TO HAVE THEIR HANDS ON IT FOR AN HOUR.

JENKINS' HANDS WERE MISSING, SO I THOUGHT THE KILLER HAD TAKEN THEM TO USE ON THE SAFE.

I THOUGHT ABOUT THAT, TOO.

OF COURSE YOU DID.

BUT...NO HANDS.

AND NO FINGERPRINTS, EITHER.

NOW THAT I THINK OF IT, DIDN'T THOMAS SAY IT HAD TO BE THE ENGINEER'S HANDS?

AND HE'S LOCKED IN THE ENGINE CAR. THERE'S NO WAY TO GET TO HIM.

SURE THERE IS...

...IF HE TRUSTS YOU ENOUGH TO OPEN THE DOOR AND LET YOU IN.

CHECK THIS OUT. I CAN'T GET THE BACK DOOR TO OPEN.

PULL PULL

WE'LL SEE ABOUT THAT!!

WELL, NO, MAGGY, YOU SEE—

WHAMMA-RAMMA

I'D SAY IT'S FUSED.

OR...IT'S NOT REALLY A DOOR.

THERE'S NO CRACK, NO OPENING... NUTHIN'.

SHAKE-A SHAKE-A

I HAVE AN IDEA.

MR. MERLE, SIR, COULD YOU CAST "DISCERNMENT OF MAGICKS" AGAIN?

SURE THING! DI—

WHOA, WHOA, WHOA! TWICE IN ONE DAY?

THAT MIGHT BE A LITTLE ABOVE YOUR PAY GRADE, MY DUDE. I'LL DO IT.

JESS' AX!

I'M THE ONLY ONE WHO CAN USE MY AX AND I HAVE AN ALIBI.

WHAT ABOUT THE ALASKAN KING CRAB BACK THERE? MAYBE HE SNIPPED IT OFF WITH HIS HUGE CLAW THINGS.

I DON'T THINK SO. THE CUT WAS FAR TOO CLEAN FOR THAT.

YOU ARE SO RIGHT! THE CHOICE OF A BLADE IS SO-O-O-O DAMNED IMPORTANT.

"IT'S GOTTA BE KEEN IF IT'S GONNA BE CLEAN!"

I LIKE THAT! I'M GONNA STEAL THAT!

A-HEM.

MAYBE SOMEONE USED THE TELEPORTATION ROD TO SEND HIS HEAD SOMEWHERE...BUT NOT HIS BODY.

WOULD THAT DO IT?

LISTEN!

I'M HAVING A MOMENT OF GENIUS AND I DON'T WANT TO WASTE IT!

JENKINS KILLED THE ENGINEER—

—HUDSON.

RIGHT.

JENKINS KILLED HUDSON HAWK AND TOOK THE HEAD SO THE BODY COULDN'T BE IDENTIFIED!

HE SWITCHED CLOTHES WITH HIM AND CHOPPED OFF HIS HANDS SO HE COULD USE THEM TO OPEN THE CRYPTSAFE!

HE'S AFTER OUR BOOTY!

NOT THE BOOTY!!

DRINK SERVICE!

WELL, YOU'RE OUT OF LUCK THERE, BUT I BET THERE'S A CAPRI SUN IN THE KITCHEN?

NO! THAT'S HOW JENKINS GOT TO THE ENGINEER! DURING DRINK SERVICE!

"JENKINS INCAPACITATED HUDSON, STUFFED HIM UNDER THE DRINK CART..."

"AND WE WERE ALL SO PREOCCUPIED BACK ON PAGE 75, WE DIDN'T NOTICE A THING!"

"JENKINS HAULED HIM BACK, CREATED THE PORT..."

"ZIP-ZOPP-ZOOP! OFF WITH HIS HEAD!"

"AND THE LAST THING HE TOOK WAS POOR HUDSON'S HANDS."

YOU SIRS SHOWED UP BEFORE HE COULD FINISH.

WHEN THE FIRE CRAB MADE YOU RUN AWAY—

HEY! IT WAS A STRATEGIC WITHDRAWAL!

—SORRY, SIR. AFTER YOU STRATEGICALLY WITHREW, HE HAD THE CRAB BURN UP THE BODY, SO WE COULDN'T TELL WHO IT REALLY WAS.

THAT IS *CLASSIC* JENKINS.

HAVING THE CRAB DO IT SO HE DIDN'T HAVE TO USE A SPELL SLOT.

HAHA!

I GOT SUSPICIOUS WHEN THE "ENGINEER" KNEW THE VICTIM HAD BEEN BEHEADED.

HOW WOULD HE KNOW THAT?

THEN THAT WAS *JENKINS* ON THAT SPEAKER THING, NOT HUDSON!

HE'S STILL IN THE ENGINEER'S CAR!!

LET'S GET HIM!!!

HE'S NOT THERE, IS HE?

NO, SIR. HE PROBABLY TOOK THE DRINK CART WITH POOR MR. HUDSON'S HANDS TO THE BACK OF THE TRAIN.

JENKINS WAS USING MAGIC TO TALK TO YOU.

GHOSTLY VOICE
→PROJECTS AND RECEIVES VOICES
→SIMULATES CONVERSATION
→HANDY PLOT DEVICE

OF COURSE, HE FOOLED YOUR ASSES, TOO.

I REALLY THOUGHT I WAS GOING TO BE BETTER AT THIS DETECTIVE STUFF...

Chapter 6

YOU'RE GONNA LEVITATE HIM?

YEAH!

WE TIE A ROPE TO HIM. I LEVITATE HIM. HE HORIZONTALLY RAPPELS DOWN THE SIDE OF THE TRAIN TO THE CABOOSE DOOR!

LET ME MAKE ONE ADDENDUM TO YOUR PLAN HERE, TAAKO.

CAST LEVITATE SPECIFICALLY ON MY MAGIC JUMPING BOOTS.

THAT WAY I CAN KICK THEM OFF IF I NEED TO.

I LOVE IT! IT'S *DELECTABLE.* LET'S DO IT.

I GOTTA ADMIT, AT LEAST IT'LL BE FUN TO WATCH...

...AS YOU PING-PONG BACK AND FORTH BETWEEN THE TRAIN AND TUNNEL.

YOU STILL HORNY FOR IT?

AHEM.

THERE IS...

...LETTERMAN'S GAP.

HEIST PLANNING! I LOVE HEIST PLANNING!!

THE TRAIN WILL EMERGE FROM THIS SECTION OF THE TEETH AND CROSS OVER ON A SUSPENDED RAIL LINE BEFORE REENTERING THE MOUNTAINS.

AND THAT LAST TUNNEL GOES STRAIGHT TO EVERSUMMER.

LETTERMAN'S GAP IS THE ONLY TIME THE LIMITED WILL BE OUT IN THE OPEN BEFORE IT REACHES THE CITY.

HOW LONG WILL HE HAVE?

AT THE SPEED THE TRAIN'S MOVING NOW...

...FIGURING THE TOTAL SPATIAL DISPLACEMENT BY THE VELOCITY OF THE BODY...SPECIFYING THE VECTOR AND DIRECTION...

...NINETY SECONDS?

IF WE'RE LUCKY.

SHIT. I REALLY WANTED TO BE CLOONEY, BUT I'M THE ACROBAT, AREN'T I?

YOU'RE THE ACROBAT.

POP!

...OF COURSE YOU'RE *SMART* ENOUGH TO REALIZE THAT THE ACROBAT IS THE MOST IMPORTANT PART OF THE PLAN...?

MAGNUS IS *SO* ON BOARD WITH THIS PLAN!!

WHAT ARE WE SUPPOSED TO DO WITH THIS?

TIE IT TO SOMETHING BOLTED DOWN.

WHY DON'T WE JUST HOLD IT?

I DON'T TRUST YOU GOOFUSES.

HARD TO ARGUE WITH THAT.

YEAH. IT SEEMS LIKE A LOT OF WORK. AND WE MIGHT GET BORED.

SOUNDS LIKE US.

MR. MAGNUS, I JUST ALCHEMIZED SOMETHING THAT MIGHT COME IN HANDY.

IT'S A MAGIC BEAN. IF YOU POP IT INTO YOUR MOUTH YOU'LL BECOME IMMENSELY HEAVY.

IT MIGHT HELP YOU IF YOU FEEL LIKE YOU'RE ABOUT TO FLY OFF THE TRAIN.

BEAN of HEFT
+SPELL+
+increases weight, apparently
+saliva activated

THANKS, GRAHAM!

BUT IF YOU THINK I'M GOING TO TRADE YOU MY PET COW FOR THIS...

...YOU'RE IN THE WRONG STORY.

150

WHOOMFT!

HUH. MEAT MONSTERS WITH ONE ELVEN HAND EACH...

NOT MY PARTICULAR KINK, BUT HEY, YOU DO YOU, JENKY!

WOBBLE

SLAMSH!

FLAMES OF HOLINESS
→ Fire and Radiant damage
→ Really FUCKS up the undead

FWOOSH!

WHOOMF!

SIZZLE

PAT PAT

RRR GRRLA HHRR?

THIS IS *NOT POSSIBLE!*

HOW DID YOU SEE THROUGH MY PERFECT CRIME?

WELL...

...A FOURTH GRADER HELPED US.

JENKINS
RACE   ELF
Class   WIZARD
(more powerful than we thought)
+ PROFICIENCIES +
→ Teleportation magic
→ Meat Monster Wrangling
→ Body Horror

163

THWAQUELCH!!

SHHFFRRZZZZ!

NO-LOOK HI-5!

SPLAT!

O-O-O-O-O—

—KAY...

I SEE I'M OUTNUMBERED AND...OUT-AXED...AND OUT...UMBRELLA-ED...

I AM A BIG ENOUGH MAN TO ADMIT DEFEAT, SO HERE IS THE DEAL I WILL MAKE WITH YOU:

167

Chapter 7

GOLD-ISH COMPASS
+ DESCRIPTION +
MYSTICAL DOWSING ROD
→ POINTS to the most valuable item
→ you know, like the kid said

LIKE THIS?

I NOTICED HE DROPPED IT WHEN THE MEAT MONSTER KNOCKED THE SHIT OUT OF HIM.

THE COMPASS THING IS GOING NUTS...

SPROING!

I KNOW WHAT IT'S TELLING US...

THAT JENKINS ROBBED MR. PEANUT?

NO! IT'S THE MONOCLE! THAT'S GOTTA BE THE THING!

WELL THEN, TAAKO... YOU'D BETTER GRAB IT.

ME?

YOU RESISTED THE THRALL ON THE GAUNTLET! I BET YOU CAN DO IT AGAIN!

YEAH! WE BELIEVE IN YOU... CHAMP!

FWIP

FWIP

FWIP

FWIP

FINE...

YOU BUNCHA BABIES.

CATCH!

KHHK

MAGNUS... COME IN MAGNUS.

HEY! WE GOT BARS!!

KILLIAN! YOU WON'T BELIEVE THIS!! I'M HAVING THE COOLEST TIME!!

I SOLVED A MURDER AND GOT TO MEET JESS THE BEHEADER AND THERE WAS THIS GIANT-ASS CRAB—

I'M SORRY, MAGNUS CAN'T COME TO THE STONE RIGHT NOW BECAUSE HE'S STARING IMMINENT DEATH AND MASSIVE DESTRUCTION IN THE FACE!!!!

HE'LL GET BACK TO YOU!

...MAYBE.

GRAB!

FLIP

SNAP!

WE HAVE TO GET INTO THE ENGINEER'S CAR AND STOP IT *NOW!!*

AS USUAL, IT'S UP TO ME TO SAVE THE DAMNED DAY!

...BY USING A POWERFUL MAGICAL ITEM I KNOW NOTHING ABOUT.

ARE YOU *SHITTING* ME? I'M TAAKO, BABY! TAAAAKO!

SLAYER OF SPIDERS! CHARMER OF BUGBEARS! FREEZER OF MEAT MONSTERS!!

TRUST ME!

...

JINGLE!

IS THIS FAKE CONFIDENCE YOUR ATTEMPT TO PROTECT ME BY GETTING ME TO JUMP...?

...OR TO DISTRACT ME FROM THAT BAG OF STUFF YOU TOOK FROM THE SAFE?

HEY, LOOK AT THAT! YOU FINALLY SOLVED A MYSTERY.

YOU KNOW WHAT?

FUCK IT!

I DO TRUST YOU!

ME TOO...

I JUST CAN'T REACH ANY HIGHER.

...YOU **CAN** DO THIS, RIGHT?

MAN, I DON'T KNOW...

OUR TRACK RECORD WITH HEROIC DEEDS IS PRETTY LOUSY.

NO NO NO NO. YOU'RE APPROACHING IT ALL WRONG.

DON'T THINK OF THIS AS PRESERVING PROPERTY AND SAVING A BUNCH OF LIVES...

...THINK OF IT AS USING THAT TELEPORT ROD TO REALLY FUCK SOME PLACE UP WITH A TRAIN.

...*THAT,* I CAN DO.

189

Chapter 8

HEY! YOU THREE!

ARTEMIS STERLING, LORD OF EVERSUMMER, HAS QUESTIONS FOR YOU!

AHEM.

WHAT—

IT'S ALL RIGHT, SIR...

...THEY'RE WITH ME.

LORD ARTEMIS STERLING
RACE: HUMAN
CLASS: ROYALTY-TYPE GUY
+ PROFICIENCIES +
→ RULING
→ ADMINISTRATING
→ HAVING AN AWESOME NAME

...SEEMS LIKE A LOT OF AUTHORITY TO GIVE TO A KID...

WE DID IT, SIRS! WE SOLVED THE CASE.

THEN WHY DON'T YOU LOOK HAPPY, SHORT-PANTS?

I'M JUST KIND OF SAD BECAUSE I WAS TRANSPORTING MY GRANDPA'S FAVORITE SILVERWARE HOME FROM THE CLEANERS.

I DIDN'T THINK TO GRAB IT FROM THE CRYPTSAFE.

HE TOLD ME "I'D LIKE TO SEE THAT SILVERWARE ONE MORE TIME BEFORE I DIE...!"

FUNNY YOU SHOULD MENTION THAT...

199

YOU SAID...

..."GRAND RELICS..."?

THAT'S RIGHT...

THE GRAND RELICS ARE POWERFUL WEAPONS CREATED BY THE... RED ROBES.

A BAND OF WIZARDS, WARLOCKS, AND OTHER MAGIC USERS WHO WERE CARELESS WITH THEIR...MAGICAL EXPERIMENTATIONS.

THE RESULT OF THOSE EXPERIMENTS WAS THE CREATION OF WHAT WE CALL THE SEVEN GRAND RELICS.

THE BUREAU'S PURPOSE— MY PURPOSE— IS DESTROYING THEM.

FIVE.

WE'VE BROUGHT YOU...TWO RELICS.

...THAT LEAVES... FIVE, RIGHT?

YOU'RE RIGHT. FIVE.

FIVE RELICS REMAIN, AND THE RED ROBES WILL DO ANYTHING TO WIN THEM BACK.

HOLD UP.

SO YOU'RE TELLING US THAT YOU AND YOUR BIG ORGANIZATION AND SECRET MOON BASE AND FLYING SNOW GLOBES, HAVE BEEN DOING THIS FOR HOWEVER LONG...

AND YOUR SCORE IS *ZERO?!*

TWO?

NO! THAT'S *OUR* SCORE!

YOU, ME, AND BEEFCAKE O'BURLY OVER THERE!

BOB INCORPORATED HAS A BIG OLD GOOSE EGG!

WHAT *EXACTLY* IS YOUR POINT, TAAKO?

MY POINT IS: I ONLY SIGNED UP FOR THIS GIG BECAUSE I THOUGHT YOU *KNEW* WHAT YOU WERE *DOING!*

YOU OWE US SOME *ANSWERS!*

WHERE'D YOU FIND A GIANT BRAINWASHING JELLYFISH?

WHY DON'T THE RED ROBES JUST KILL US?

AND WHO MADE YOU THE BOSS OF MAGIC WEAPONS, ANYWAY?!

WHAT'S *YOUR* STORY, MADAME DIRECTOR?!

TAAKO...?

I KNOW YOU HAVE QUESTIONS—A *LOT* OF QUESTIONS...

AND WE WILL ANSWER THEM *ALL.*

JUST MAYBE... TOMORROW MORNING...?

AFTER YOU'VE HAD A CHANCE TO REST...?

DON'T STOP... ON MY ACCOUNT... I FEEL...AWESOME.

SHUT UP! YOU DO NOT. DYING REALLY TAKES IT OUT OF A PERSON.

OKAY. FINE.

FINE.

TOMORROW.

TOMORROW.

WAIT!

WHERE DID YOU FIND THAT UMBRELLA?

THIS?

I FOUND IT LIKE TWO ADVENTURES AGO!

ON SOME SKELETON IN A CAVE.

SEE? ANSWERING SOMEONE'S QUESTION ISN'T HARD AT ALL...

...IS IT?

211

Fan Art Gallery

The *Adventure Zone* has been lucky enough to garner a passionate and deeply creative fandom. Many thanks to the fan artists who contributed pieces to this gallery—and to all the writers, artists, creators, and fans of all stripes who have made *The Adventure Zone* what it is.

The ADVENTURE CONTINUES in

THE ADVENTURE ZONE Petals to the Metal

Coming Soon!

My Murphy

Gene McKechnie

Star Prichard

Pola Kowalewska

Sara Cliclicman

Glowbat

Phoebe Ayscough

Karoline Stjernfelt

Devon Pasternak